# TARGETS · AGE 8-9

# Science
## at the Circus
## Richard Dawson

WALKER BOOKS
LONDON

# NOTE TO PARENTS

### What is the National Curriculum?

● This is the government's overall plan for school work from age 5 to 16. It clearly outlines the subjects that children will be taught and the aims, or *targets*, to be achieved in each subject.

● English, Maths and Science are the core subjects of the curriculum and children at primary school will spend about 10% of their time on each of them.

● As part of the plan, your child will be assessed at ages 7, 11, 14 and 16. This is to measure their level of progress within each subject and tackle any difficulties.

### Will this series help me understand the National Curriculum?

● Yes, this series has been designed specially to help you understand the type and standard of work children will be doing with the National Curriculum.

● The series covers Maths, English and Science and is based on the Attainment Targets (what children should know or do) laid down in each subject.

● Each page of the book covers part of one Attainment Target, and provides lively activities for your child which are both fun to do and give practice in the particular target.

● The area of Science covered by the Attainment Target is labelled at the top of the page, like this:

> Materials

(Note: these are simplified versions of the actual Attainment Target titles.)

● The relevant part of the Attainment Target is quoted, in full, at the foot of the page, so you know exactly what the National Curriculum requires. (These do contain some jargon, but the activity helps make things clear.)

● This book includes all the Attainment Targets for Level 3 (average 9 years). Target 1, which is on the skills needed for exploring and investigating, is covered as far as possible in the activities for the other targets.

### Should I help my child with the activities?

● Yes, by all means. Treat these activities as a game, not a test, and enjoy them together. In some cases you may need to help with reading the instructions.

● Don't force your child to do the activities if he or she doesn't feel like it. It's better to find 10 minutes when they're keen and fresh than half an hour when they're tired and jaded.

### What does the scoring mean?

● Not all the activities have set answers. For those that do, the scoring is for fun, and gives some guide to how your child is getting on. You can help check the answers on page 32 and give one point for each correct answer. The score can then be coloured in, or ticked on the special score table at the foot of the page:

SCORE 〉〉〉〉〉〉〉〉

● These books are *not* like the tests that schools will use for assessment in the National Curriculum. Practical investigations are a vital part of Science which cannot be tested easily from a book. However, the activities can give you some guide to your child's understanding and point out areas of weakness which may need further practice.

### What do I do if my child finds these activities difficult?

● First and foremost, be encouraging not critical.

● This book covers work for an *average* 9 year old, but the level of attainment of a *real* 9 year old is very varied. It could be that your child is simply not ready for the work covered or needs more practical experience.

● If your child continues to have problems, try to find ways for more practice or talk it over with the teacher.

First published 1991
by Walker Books Ltd
87 Vauxhall Walk
London SE11 5HJ

© text and illustrations Richard Dawson 1991

Prepared for Walker Books by Multi Lingua, London
Editors: Elizabeth Small and Catherine Bruzzone
Design: Walker Books, Sarah Amit, Naomi Games
Cover illustration: David Anstey

Typeset by Parker Typesetting Service, Leicester

Printed and bound in Hong Kong by
Sheck Wah Tong Printing Press Ltd.

British Library Cataloguing in Publication Data
is available from the British Library

ISBN 0-7445-1879-2

The circus is coming to town! Colour in all the living things in this picture.

Think about how all the living things are similar and how they are different.

Fill in your score. Are you on target?

- be able to recognise similarities and differences among living things.

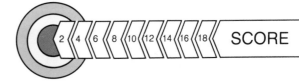

SCORE

3

First look at the picture and then divide the living things into three sets.

List your sets here.

| SET I | SET 2 | SET 3 |
|-------|-------|-------|
|       |       |       |
|       |       |       |
|       |       |       |
|       |       |       |
|       |       |       |

Now name your sets.

Fill in your score.

SCORE

• be able to sort living things into broad groups according to observable features.

4

What season is it? Tick your answers.

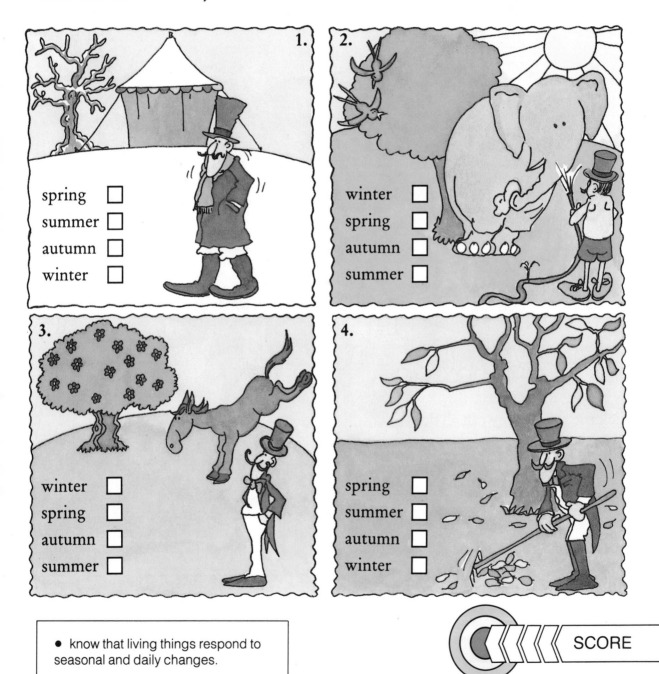

1.
spring ☐
summer ☐
autumn ☐
winter ☐

2.
winter ☐
spring ☐
autumn ☐
summer ☐

3.
winter ☐
spring ☐
autumn ☐
summer ☐

4.
spring ☐
summer ☐
autumn ☐
winter ☐

• know that living things respond to seasonal and daily changes.

SCORE

## Life

Look at these creatures.

Tick the things they can all do:

| | | | |
|---|---|---|---|
| talk | ☐ | breathe | ☐ |
| sleep | ☐ | move | ☐ |
| eat | ☐ | fly | ☐ |
| swim | ☐ | | |

Fill in your score as usual. Are you on target?

SCORE

● know that the basic life processes: feeding, breathing, movement and behaviour, are common to human beings and the other living things they have studied.

Number each member of the Wobble family, starting with the oldest.

• be able to describe the main stages in the human life cycle.

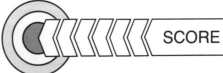

SCORE

Which posters could be true?
Write true or false on each one.

1. CIRCUS

Danny's

Dancing Dodos

_____

2. CIRCUS

See

Mighty Mammoths

_____

3. CIRCUS

FEATURING
LIVE DINOSAURS

_____

4. CIRCUS
The one and only

BOXING KANGAROO

_____

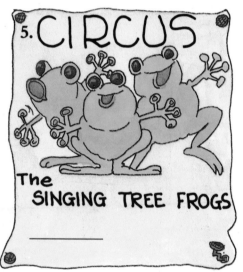

5. CIRCUS

The
SINGING TREE FROGS

_____

SCORE

• know that some life forms became
extinct a long time ago and others
more recently.

8

The circus has moved on.
How many changes do you think have been made to the site? ☐
Circle them on the picture.

Think about any potential dangers to the site.

- know that human activity may produce local changes in the Earth's surface, air and water.

SCORE

9

# CIRCUS
## Clean Up Campaign

How could you clean up your environment?
FREE CIRCUS TICKETS FOR ALL WINNING IDEAS!

- be able to give an account of a project to improve the local environment.

Imagine you are entering the competition.
What could you do to improve your environment?

_____

_____

_____

_____

_____

_____

_____

_____

_____

_____

_____

_____

_____

Here are some pages from a catalogue. Colour in the things that are made from natural materials.

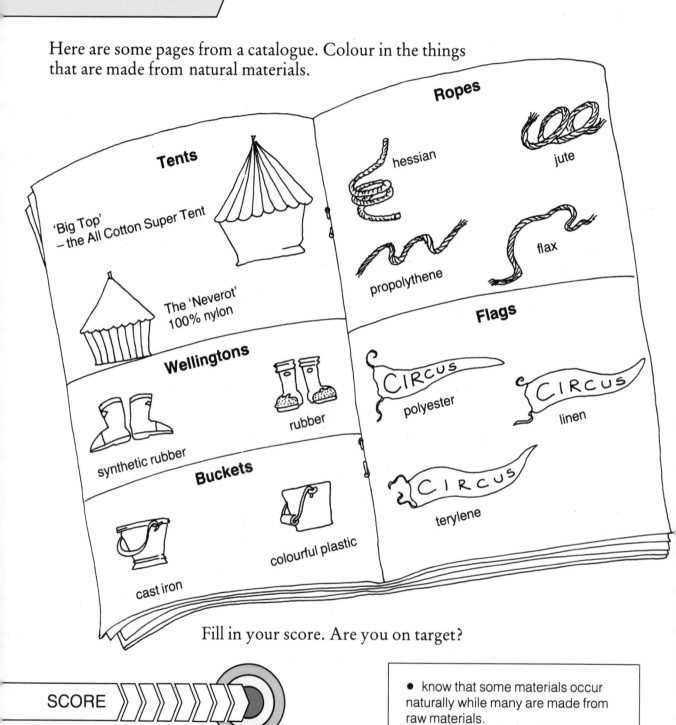

**Tents**

'Big Top' – the All Cotton Super Tent

The 'Neverot' 100% nylon

**Wellingtons**

synthetic rubber

rubber

**Buckets**

cast iron

colourful plastic

**Ropes**

hessian

jute

propolythene

flax

**Flags**

polyester

linen

terylene

Fill in your score. Are you on target?

SCORE >>>>

● know that some materials occur naturally while many are made from raw materials.

**1.** How are the materials in this picture similar?

_____

_____

_____

**2.** How are they different?

_____

_____

_____

● be able to list the similarities and
differences in a variety of everyday
materials.

SCORE

13

The Ring Master is looking at his circus. Which things are worn out?
Give them a new coat of paint by colouring them in. Then tell someone what
you think might have caused the damage.

- be able to describe from their observations some of the effects of weathering on buildings and on the landscape.

Colour yellow all the places where there is air.

Are you on target?

- know that air is all around us.

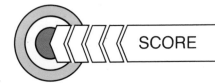

# Earth

Where would you put up the Big Top?
Draw it in.

Say why you have put it there.

_____

_____

_____

SCORE

• be able to give an account of an
investigation of some natural material
(rock or soil).

The Ring Master wants to know what the weather forecast will be for the next three performances.

| **Monday** | **Tuesday** | **Wednesday** |
|:---:|:---:|:---:|

Describe what the weather will be like on:

| **Monday** | **Tuesday** | **Wednesday** |
|:---:|:---:|:---:|

_____ _____ _____

_____ _____ _____

_____ _____ _____

_____ _____ _____

---

● be able to understand and interpret common meteorological symbols as used in the media.

17

# Forces

Draw an arrow on each picture to show the direction of each force of movement.

**1.**

**2.**

**3.**

**4.**

SCORE

- understand that when things are changed in shape, begin to move or stop moving, forces are acting on them.

Which of the sea lions' toys will float and which will sink?
Write your answer beside each toy.

1. _____

4. _____

2. _____

3. _____

5. _____

6. _____

7. _____

Fill in your score as usual.

● understand the factors which
cause objects to float or sink in water.

SCORE

Sparks, the electrician, is trying to fix a spotlight, but his wire is too short.

What can he use to make the connection? Tick your answer.

A piece of rope ☐
A rubber hose ☐
A piece of fuse wire ☐
A cable ☐

SCORE

• know that some materials conduct electricity well while others do not.

Sparks has gone to fetch more cable to fix the spotlight. He has left a drawing for his apprentice to fix up a light in the Ring Master's caravan, but he has forgotten to draw in the wires.

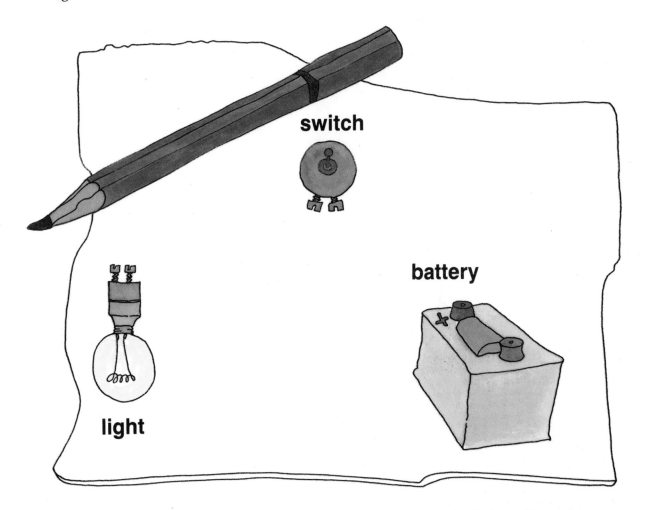

Can you draw in the wires to complete the circuit so that the light will work?

- understand that a complete circuit is needed for an electrical device, such as a bulb or buzzer, to work.

SCORE

**1.** How could this interview be recorded?  _____

**2.** How long do you think this trick will last?
How could this be measured?  _____

**3.** How could the circus records be stored,
other than in books?  _____

SCORE

- be able to store information using devices, for example, *a tape recorder, and a digital watch*.

- know that information can be stored electronically in a variety of ways, for example, *text, number, pictures and sound*.

What makes each of these go?

Fill in your score as usual.

- understand in qualitative terms that models and machines need a source of energy in order to work.

SCORE

If the thermometer is showing hot, colour it red. If it is showing cold, colour it blue.

1.

2.

3.

4.

SCORE

● know that the temperature is a measure of how hot (or cold) things are.

Draw in the belts needed to get the tent up!

- be able to use simple power sources (electric motors, rubber bands) and devices which transfer energy (gears, belts, levers).

SCORE

**1.** Could this fan tell if the circus is coming by listening to the ground?
Tick your answer.

Yes ☐
No ☐

Write the reason for your answer here.

_____

_____

**2.** The Ring Master is using a simple device to talk to the clown in the next tent.
Will it work?

Yes ☐
No ☐

Write the reason for your answer here.

_____

_____

SCORE

● know that sounds are produced by vibrating objects and can travel through different materials.

How does each instrument make its sound?

1.

2.

3.

Fill in your score. Are you on target?

- be able to give a simple explanation of the way in which sound is generated and can travel through different materials.

SCORE

# Light

The spotlight is shining on to some mirrors. Draw in the path of the reflected beam of light.

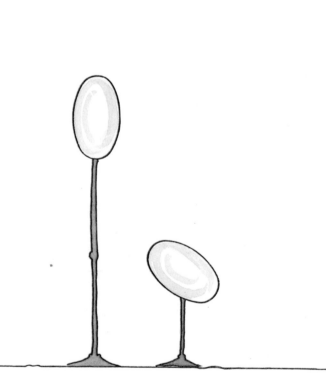

Is the clown in the spotlight?  | YES | NO |

● know that light can be made to change direction and shiny surfaces can form images.

Look at yourself reflected in each side of a very shiny spoon.
Now draw the images that would be seen in these special mirrors.

**1. a concave mirror**

**2. a convex mirror**

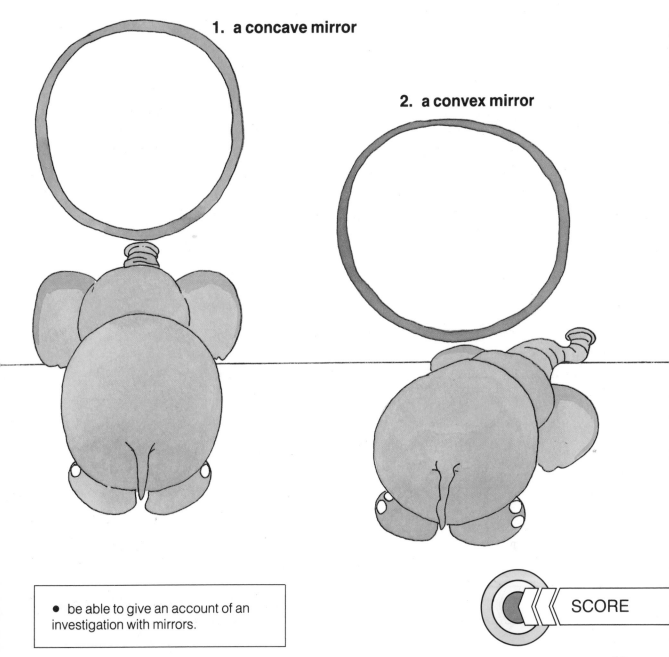

● be able to give an account of an investigation with mirrors.

SCORE

29

It is 12 o'clock midday. Draw in the approximate position of the Sun in the sky, and the shadows of the tent.

**1.** Spring

**2.** Summer

**3.** Autumn

**4.** Winter

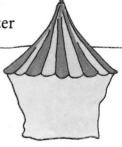

SCORE

- know that the inclination of the Sun in the sky changes during the year.

30

The Ring Master has made a sundial. What time is it in each picture?

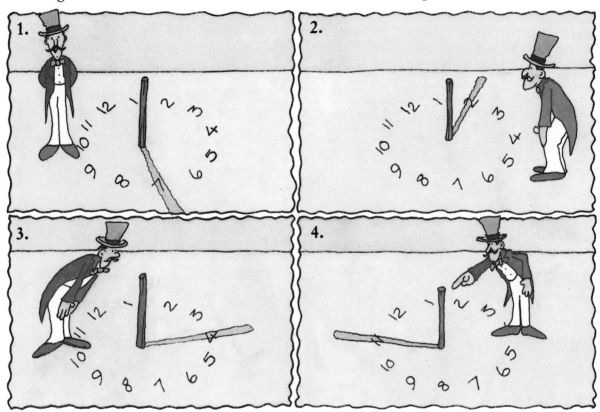

1. _____

2. _____

3. _____

4. _____

• be able to measure time with a sundial.

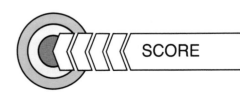

SCORE

# ANSWERS

**page 3**

There are 18 living things: 2 flowers; 3 trees; 7 people; 2 elephants; 1 cat; 1 dog and 2 birds.

**page 4**

Suggested sets are:

| Set 1 | Set 2 | Set 3 |
|---|---|---|
| Horses | Lion | Clown |
| Zebras | Tiger | Bareback rider |
| | Cat | Attendant |

Suggested names for sets:

| Set 1 | Set 2 | Set 3 |
|---|---|---|
| Horse | Cat | Human |

**page 5**

1. Winter
2. Summer
3. Spring
4. Autumn

**page 6**

Sleep; eat; breathe; move

**page 7**

1. Grandpa Wobble
2. Mr Wobble
3. Mrs Wobble
4. Daughter Wobble
5. Son Wobble
6. Baby Wobble

**page 8**

1. False
2. False
3. False
4. True
5. True

**page 9**

6 changes: tree cut down; rubbish bags; manure; tyre marks; worn grass where tent has been; fire.

**page 12**

Natural materials: cotton; rubber; cast iron; jute; flax; hessian; linen.

**page 13**

1. All except the pegs are made from fibres.
2. You can wear some of them. Some are made from artificial materials, others from natural ones.

**page 14**

Tent and caravan due to weathering.

**page 15**

Discuss this with your child. The boxes should be coloured to show that air is all around us. NB: Balloons contain helium — a gas lighter than air.

**page 16**

The tent should go on the raised bit in front of the rocks because the ground is solid and will not flood. Also there are no rocks and the tent will be protected.

**page 17**

Monday: overcast with showers.
Tuesday: sunshine with a wind speed of 20mph.
Wednesday: rain with a wind speed of 40mph.

**page 18**

1.

2. ↓

3. ←

4. →

**page 19**

1. Sink
2. Float
3. Sink
4. Sink
5. Float
6. Float
7. Float

**page 20**

A cable

**page 21**

**page 22**

1. Tape recorder or video
2. Stop watch or digital watch
3. Computer

**page 23**

1. Wind
2. Petrol
3. Electricity
4. Man's weight

**page 24**

1. Red
2. Blue
3. Blue
4. Red

**page 25**

The belts would look like this:

**page 26**

1. Yes. Vibrations along the ground.
2. Yes. Vibrations along the string.

**page 27**

1. The drum skin vibrates.
2. Air vibrates in the metal tube of the trumpet.
3. The cello strings vibrate.

**page 28**

Yes. Suggested paths are:

**page 29**

Suggested images:

1.

2.

**page 30**

**page 31**

1. 7.00 am or 7.00 pm
2. 2.00 pm
3. 4.00 pm
4. 11.00 am